DOWN AFRICAN ROADS

Written by **Judy Langley**
Illustrated by **Wendy Kikugawa**

New Hope
Birmingham, Alabama

New Hope
P.O. Box 12065
Birmingham, AL 35202-2065

© 1997 by New Hope

Printed in the United States of America
Dewey Decimal Classification: CE
Subject Headings: AFRICA—JUVENILE LITERATURE
                                      MISSIONARY KIDS
Series: Land Far Away
ISBN: 1-56309-218-2
N978106•0597•5M1

Dedication

To our parents and families for the
Christian heritage they have given us.

Where I grew up
In a land far away,
My missionary parents
Had adventures every day.

In our dusty old truck
All dented and gray,
I bounced on the bumpy
Rough roads on our way.

I watched as my parents
Greeted people each day,
I'd clap my hands too,
In the most polite way.

There was preaching each Sunday
In all different places,
'Neath thatched roofs or shingles
To kind, smiling faces.

My favorite church
Met under a tree,
Just green leaves above us,
Blue sky, birds, and bees.

Mom sewed with the women,
I played in the sand.
Sticks, stones, and doodle bugs,
My church was so grand!

Dad also taught Bible
And English each day,
Helping the students
To follow God's way.

When afternoon came
With its tropical heat,
We read books together
Building memories so sweet.

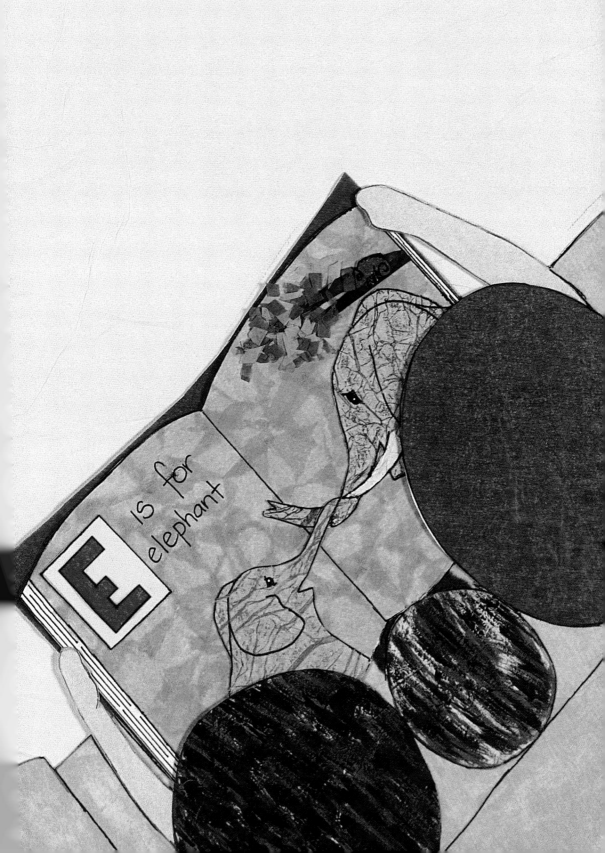

Once in a while
We needed a break,
And a trip to the city
Was all it would take.

Things to do in town

Pick up:
✓1) newspaper
2) nails – school
✓3) light bulbs – hospital
4) bookmark
5) battery
6) groceries
7) clothes and ✓shoes

Run errands

Credit for this natio
markable transformatio
to Preside l Ram
often-un er
al w
C erce h
herited i
from a series o
and coup atten
by a Muslim in
leftist guerrilla
ing from tha
el ere he
apidl
ele crisi
vate mpar
ating lan
healthy
the na
brok

Vacations were special,
I looked forward all year
To camping in game parks
With animals near.

We'd name all the animals,
Which always was fun.
Then we'd head back toward hom
In the late evening sun.

I'd pile my bed high
With furry friends dear.
Then we'd say prayers together
And thank God we were here.

Yes, I grew up
Thanking God every day
For all these adventures
In a land far away.

SUGGESTED ACTIVITIES

Participate in the following activities to help you and your child develop an awareness of other cultures.

Illustration Interaction: Do you know what a chameleon is? It is an animal that can change the color of its skin, usually to match its surroundings. There is a chameleon in each of the illustrations in this book. Can you find each of them?

Write to Missionaries: Missionaries often live far away from their families, so they usually enjoy receiving cards and letters from people who are praying for them. Any time is a good time to write to missionaries. Some people like to send birthday cards. Talk to your church's pastor about where to find missionaries' names and addresses. Do not expect a reply, though, as correspondence can be time consuming and expensive.

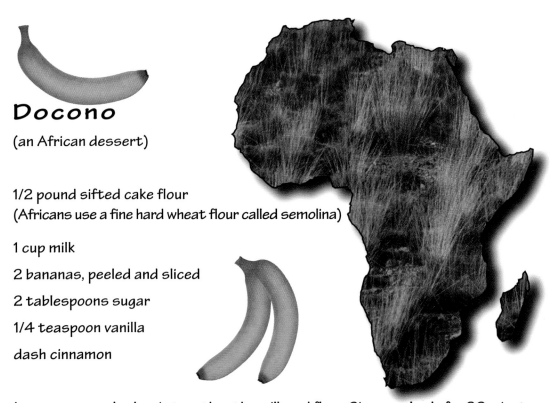

Docono

(an African dessert)

1/2 pound sifted cake flour
(Africans use a fine hard wheat flour called semolina)

1 cup milk

2 bananas, peeled and sliced

2 tablespoons sugar

1/4 teaspoon vanilla

dash cinnamon

In a saucepan, slowly mix together the milk and flour. Simmer slowly for 20 minutes, stirring constantly to avoid scorching. Do not boil. Add the other ingredients. Simmer and stir until the bananas are thoroughly warmed. Serve warm or cold.

ABOUT THE AUTHOR

From 1971 until 1983, Judy Langley and her husband, Phil, served as missionaries in Zimbabwe and Togo. Their sons Anthony and Jonathan, who both grew up in Africa, provided the inspiration for the narrations in the "Land Far Away" series. Since leaving Africa, Judy and Phil have traveled extensively doing a variety of missions work in Colorado, New Mexico, and Hawaii. Appointed by the North American Mission Board, they currently live in Fresno, California, where Phil serves as the Director of the Department of New Church Extension for the California Southern Baptist Convention.

ABOUT THE ILLUSTRATOR

Wendy Kikugawa was born and raised in Hawaii. She enjoys reading, drawing, baking, cooking, and doing all kinds of crafts. Wendy continues to be amazed at how God works in her life, and she is especially grateful for the opportunity to illustrate the "Land Far Away" series.

If you enjoyed Down African Roads, be sure not to miss The Elephant Path, Clay Homes, Bushland Backyard, and Bush Station Boys, Books One, Two, Three, and Five in the Land Far Away series. Look for these titles in your local Christian bookstore, or order them by calling 1-800-968-7301.